The Lullingstone Secret

The Lullingstone Secret

by
Jill Masters

Illustrated by Diana Malawo

The Wakeman Trust, London

THE LULLINGSTONE SECRET
© Jill Masters, 2021

THE WAKEMAN TRUST
(Wakeman Trust is a UK Registered Charity)

UK Registered Office
38 Walcot Square
London SE11 4TZ

USA Office
300 Artino Drive
Oberlin, OH 44074-1263

Website: www.wakemantrust.org

ISBN 978 1 913133 11 5

Illustrated by Diana Malawo
Cover design by Andrew Owen

Printed by CPI Group (UK) Ltd, Croydon CRO 4YY

Contents

AD 410

Fire!

Smoke rose into the air. Trees bowed under a mighty gust of wind sweeping through the valley, and the column of smoke was soon fanned into a mass of roaring flames. Anxious faces peeped from the woods as the Villa they loved was devoured by the hungry fire. They dared not hurry to the rescue, for surrounding the blazing building stood a hoard of wild, evil-looking men, well known for destroying all they found. Any who stood in their path would be dealt with in a most violent way.

An enormous thud shook the whole valley as the roof supports gave way and thousands of tiles crashed to the ground. Only charred walls remained to feed the flames. Eyes were moist as the people of the valley watched the magnificent building disintegrate into a pile of smouldering ashes. This Villa had been the mainstay of their

7

life and employment, and to many it had become the very gateway to Heaven.

At the top of the valley, looking down from afar, stood a lady, white-haired, dignified and serene, yet inwardly broken-hearted. For her, this was the burning of a lifetime's memories. She clutched closely a bundle of precious parchments, her most treasured wedding present, the one item she had chosen to snatch away before escaping for her life. Watching the flames envelop her family home, the parchments reminded her of happy days now gone, and scenes of the past began to pass before her eyes ... The smoke disappeared, and she saw in her mind's eye the Villa of Lullingstone, just as perfect as when she had first caught a glimpse of it seventy years ago as an excited seven-year-old ...

Part I
AD 340

Chapter I

Cause for Excitement

Lydia was the daughter of a wealthy merchant, living in Londinium near the Forum, a large plaza with the Baths and market place. Their home was a single-storied house built round a graceful courtyard, with white Grecian pillars at the entrance, and many servants within, cooking, cleaning and obeying her parents' every command.

Each morning as the day dawned, her father, Lucius, threw his cloak around his shoulders, fastened it with a gold buckle, and proceeded to the Baths. There he met with his influential friends, enjoying the pleasures of bathing in luxury before beginning the important business of the day – buying, selling and arranging for valuable cargoes to be shipped to Gaul, Spain, Italy, and as far away as Syria. When Lydia's elder brother Marcus was fifteen, he joined him, beginning to learn his father's trade. But trade was not the chief concern of Marcus. His great interest was wrestling, and he longed for the afternoon to come to prove himself against newly arrived competitors.

One sunny day in early May, Lydia's mother, Flavia, was very busy. The servants were hurrying from one room to another with piles of neatly folded clothes, boxes of food and wine, while outside the horses were being shod. Seven-year-old Lydia was intrigued by all this bustle, sensing something exciting was happening. The adults were whispering amongst themselves, but as yet no one had told her what it was all about.

Balbus, her nine-year-old brother, was equally mystified. 'Perhaps Pater will tell us the secret when he comes home,' they hoped. But when Lucius arrived home early that afternoon he only answered their pleas and questions with a knowing smile. 'Patience, my little ones. All will be told you before you retire to sleep, I promise,' was all he would say.

The longer evenings had come. The servants had stopped stoking the heating system, and Lydia was choosing new dresses for the summer months. Already she had her own ideas about what she liked to wear.

Marcus was often out with his friends, wining and dining and enjoying their company, so there were only four at table that evening: Lucius and Flavia, Lydia and Balbus. Lucius promised that as long as he did not hear a single question during the meal, he would answer all their questions afterwards. The servants cleared the table, and the family sat on couches around a bowl of fresh, juicy fruit collected from an Italian ship that very day. As Balbus sucked an orange, Lydia could contain herself no longer. 'Well, what is it, Pater? Please tell us everything, Mater!'

Lucius put his arm round her and pulled her on to his knee. With a twinkle in his eye he asked, 'How would you like a ride into the countryside?' Lydia squealed with joy, jumping up and throwing her arms around his neck. 'Why, of course we would. Can we go tomorrow?'

'If you are good, and go to bed early,' Lucius replied. And then added calmly, 'And tell your tutor which games you want to take because we shall be staying a few weeks.'

'A few weeks? But where?' 'Are we staying with a friend?' 'Can Marcus come too?' 'Shall I take my new gown?' The questions tumbled out from Lydia and Balbus.

Lucius wondered which question to answer first, so he nodded at Flavia. She told the two restless bundles of energy to sit down quietly so that she could try to explain. 'Remember that Pater was away from home for several weeks earlier this year,' she began. Lydia and Balbus nodded, their attention riveted. Now the mystery of their father's absence would be solved.

He had been visiting their grandparents' large farm in Kent. Balbus remembered the sad time when, as a little boy, he had travelled to the farm with his parents for the funeral of his uncle and aunt, both victims of a deadly epidemic that had swept the Roman Empire.

'Grandfather is growing old,' continued Flavia, 'and can no longer manage the work of the farm on his own. He has decided to retire and move away. So now the Villa, the fields and the woods will be our home in the country!'

This elegant Villa had once been the splendid home of a wealthy Roman who had returned to Italy. After lying derelict for almost eighty years, their grandfather had restored the building, made it his home and farmed the land around it. The farm was such a success Grandfather was able to send Lucius away to school in Londinium for a Roman education. The whole family felt the benefits now, as Lucius had prospered so well in business he would have ample time and money to look after the farm.

'But what has Pater been doing while he was away? Why has he been to the farm?' insisted Lydia.

'That you will be able to see for yourselves tomorrow. So go to bed now and be up early in the morning,' Flavia replied in a tantalising way.

So Lydia and Balbus went straight to bed, but they did not fall asleep until late. Their minds were full of ideas as they began to take in all Mater had told them. At last they could think no longer and their heads lay still on their pillows. Inside those sleepy heads, all sorts of exciting adventures were being dreamed, but none of them could come true until the morning.

Chapter II

Journey to Lullingstone

Soon after breakfast next morning the chariot drew up before the white columns of their house. Lucius and Flavia had left early and the children were to follow with their tutor. They must not neglect their education even while they were away.

The tutor, Septimus, was a tall, thin man with a stoop. Balbus did not like him. He seemed more interested in books than teaching children. Often he was irritable and bad-tempered with Lydia and Balbus, but full of charm and grace in the presence of their parents. But just now the children had forgotten everything except the excitement of the day ahead.

The chariot turned sharply right, then left, threading its way through the chequerboard pattern of the Londinium streets, passing shops with queues of customers. As they reached the River Thames, they saw the Roman soldiers mounting guard at the tollhouse by the bridge. Septimus paid their dues and soon they reached the southern bank.

The chariot sped swiftly along the well-paved Watling Street and the city wall disappeared into the distance behind them. Balbus and Lydia eagerly gazed across the countryside, not wanting to miss a single detail. Cheerfully they waved at a group of slaves heaving stones on to a road being repaired, watched over by Roman soldiers, their helmets and breastplates glinting in the sun. The centurion in charge was not amused, but some of the slaves returned their smile.

'How far is it *now*?' Septimus was continually being asked. But when the chariot slowed down, took a right-hand turn and splashed its way across a ford, Balbus squeezed Lydia's hand and whispered, 'Almost there.' Soon they were riding on a narrow, bumpy road between the cornfields, where the young shoots were already sprouting up. Occasionally the children could spot men at work in the fields.

An excited cry went up as they rounded a bend in the road, and there before them stood Lullingstone Villa, a large, sprawling house with its red-tiled roof brightening up the whole landscape. Behind the Villa, Balbus recognised the fine Temple-Mausoleum where his uncle and aunt lay buried. The children were impatient to get out and explore their new home, but Septimus said firmly, 'Not yet.'

It was as the chariot drew into the front driveway that Balbus spotted a grubby face with tangled hair peering out of a laurel bush. He saw it only for a second, but the bright, mischievous eyes endeared their owner to him straightaway. He said nothing to Septimus but quietly decided that, as soon as possible, he would discover to whom those eyes belonged. But for now, that would have to wait.

The horse was brought to a halt. The children jumped to the ground and rushed like a pair of yelping dogs over to Lucius and Flavia, who stood in the doorway waiting to greet them. Not content with having reached their new home, they wanted to explore inside.

'First, a wash after your dusty journey,' Flavia insisted. Lydia and Balbus were soon splashing one another in the large heated bath. The steamy room was lined with cheerful tiles. The rich Roman general who formerly made this his country home had spared no expense, and the suite of bathing rooms reminded the children of the Baths at the Forum in Londinium. It was great fun to have the rooms all to themselves. They pranced from the Hot Room to the Tepid Room, and Balbus was ready to pour a jugful of icy water over Lydia as she found her way along to the Cold Room.

Once the children were dressed, Flavia took each by the hand and led them along a corridor to a large and

beautiful archway covered by a heavy curtain. 'Close your eyes. Do not look until I say!' She lifted the curtain and led them 'blindfold' for a few steps into the room.

'Now you can see what Pater has been doing,' she said. 'What do you think of our new room?' For the first time that day the children were speechless and motionless. It was too much for them to take in. They found themselves in a large room, almost a hall, and at their feet spread an enormous and colourful picture, all in mosaic tiles. They stood rooted to the spot and gazed and gazed.

Suddenly Lydia returned to life. 'A yellow lion, breathing fire – and it has a serpent's tail!' She gasped and ran forward to look at this fiendish little monster being killed by a handsome god riding a winged horse, a galloping figure spread right across the centre of the mosaic.

Next it was Balbus's turn to spring into action. He recognised the horseshoe-shaped picture, which formed the floor of the Dining Room, from a story which Septimus had read to him. 'This is the goddess Juno!' He told Lydia about the anger of the goddess when she discovered her husband Jupiter had changed into a white bull so he might carry off the fair maiden Europa across the seas to the island of Crete. Balbus admired the strong, elegant bull pictured at his feet, wondering how anyone could make such a perfect design out of thousands of tiny tiles.

The more they looked at the great floor, the more

they discovered. Strange sea creatures, hea... patterns of all kinds and even words had b... this huge carpet of stone. Only Septimus ... 'The work here by this artist is inferior – a ...un to the masterly skill of the first artist.' Lydia and Balbus thought it was unkind of him to point this out to Flavia, even if it were true.

No sooner was their late lunch cleared away than Balbus begged to be allowed to explore outside. He had seldom been into the wide-open countryside and wanted to see the secrets of nature for himself. Perhaps they might even come across the boy he had seen in the laurel bush.

Lydia was more shy. The countryside seemed very big to her and she was frightened of animals, having been brought up in the town. She certainly was not keen on insects and the other little creatures which made their home among the trees and hedgerows.

Pater gave them permission, 'As long as you do not go far. And Balbus, promise to stay close to your sister!'

They were wandering down a nearby lane, picking the colourful wild flowers which lay at their feet, when Lydia let out a cry of glee, 'How beautiful!' To the left lay a wood and beneath the trees, fresh with their new green leaves, lay a carpet of bluebells. She called Balbus, and together they filled their arms with the long pale stems topped with their sweetly scented bells of blue.

'What's that?' Balbus's sharp ears picked up the rustling sound of leaves. 'Who's there?' he demanded.

..hen a small stone came hurtling past Lydia's left ear, followed by a piercing shriek, like a war cry.

Lydia screamed and threw herself to the ground, the bluebells cushioning her fall. But Balbus stood with eyes wide open, searching in the undergrowth for the source of this commotion. As the cry died down, he fleetingly saw a figure dressed in a dull brown tunic jump down from a tree, disappear into a bush and run off into the field beyond. He wanted to give chase, but Lydia was begging him to take her straight home and he had to keep his promise.

As they entered the forecourt, Flavia came out to greet them. She was delighted with the bluebells and listened as Lydia told her of the strange cry in the woods. Balbus said nothing. He wanted to investigate further but he thought it most unlikely he would be allowed out for that purpose. He diverted his mother's attention by pointing to the large Granary close by the Villa. 'What's in there?' he enquired.

Flavia beckoned the children to follow her. She had another treat in store. Much of last year's hay had been used, but in the corner of the barn were some hens. 'If you look carefully, you may find eggs for tea!'

Lydia and Balbus soon forgot their previous adventure as they rushed towards the Granary door. Barking dogs came out to greet them, sharply called to order by the Granary keeper. More gently they stepped into the gloomy building, their eyes gradually becoming accustomed to the dark. They soon found the shelves on which sat the hens, clucking as if the Emperor of Rome himself had arrived.

Lydia discovered two brown eggs lying side by side. 'Oh, they're warm!' Balbus picked his up so quickly that it smashed down on the floor, and he learned his first lesson about country life.

The evening flew by, and before long two exhausted figures were stretched out on their couches fast asleep. Balbus told himself to rise early, 'I must go and find that boy before anyone awakes.'

Chapter III

Exploring

Balbus awoke early. Already the house was a hive of industry. The servants were up, busily preparing for the banquet to be held at the Villa that evening. Marcus was expected from Londinium with several friends, and for the first time Lucius and Flavia would be able to entertain in their splendid new Villa. Servants were giving the mosaic floor its final polish before laying out the furniture, made by local craftsmen specially for the occasion.

Balbus saw his opportunity. Everyone was so occupied they would not notice him slip out of the house and into the fields. He would be back before Mater and Pater breakfasted. Lydia looked as if she would sleep till

22

midday unless roused. He lifted the latch of a gate at the back of the house, peered around to make sure no one was watching, and raced across the courtyard, over the fence and into the field beyond.

In his hand he held a mirror and a model of a Roman ship, two items he thought might be of use to him now. He struggled to walk in the long, damp grass, so followed a path at the edge of the cornfield. Noticing a puff of smoke rising above a woodland copse, he headed in that direction and found his way to the opposite side of the wood. From behind a large, knotted oak he surveyed the surroundings.

Before him stretched a wooden fence protecting a dozen or so huts made of wood, straw and thatch. In the centre of the encampment a large fire burned, heating various pots heaped upon it. Women in short colourful tunics were cooking and laying out clothes to dry. Several men were yoking together a team of oxen, ready to take a cartload of squealing pigs to the market. Older men were making clay jugs.

Balbus realised that most of these men worked on his father's farm, but more urgently he searched the young faces, longing to catch a glimpse of those eyes which had met his only the previous day.

He was beginning to despair of ever finding them, when he noticed a small figure in a brown tunic crouched behind one of the huts. From the jerky movements he guessed the young boy was carving wood. Could this be the owner of those eyes? He picked up a pebble at his feet and carefully aimed it close to the boy's shoulder. It landed on target and two brown eyes turned inquisitively towards his.

Quickly Balbus pulled his mirror out of his pocket and using the sun's rays, flashed it in the direction of the boy who was by now standing and watching. Balbus beckoned the boy to join him. The boy hesitated for a moment, then stepped cautiously towards the fence. In a moment he was over it, and silently sliding around its circumference, edging forward yet ready at any moment to make a hasty retreat.

Balbus was sitting on a nearby tree stump, feeling a little afraid himself. He had never met country people before, having always lived amongst wealthy, highly educated Britons and Romans in the town. He pulled out his model ship. Perhaps this would attract his new friend. His plan worked, and the boy moved towards him wearing a suspicious expression mixed with curiosity. Balbus held out the model ship. The boy hesitated, then snatched it from him and held it up to the sun. Suddenly he threw it back at Balbus's feet and began to move away.

'Don't go! Don't go!' cried Balbus. Using signs and a few words they both understood, Balbus made it clear that he was giving the boat to his new friend. Gradually a smile crossed the boy's face. Balbus, who spoke Latin, found it difficult to follow the dialect of the country boy, though it did not take him long to discover that the boy's name was Rufus and he had lived in the

encampment all his life.

Before long the two boys had lost their shyness and were off exploring the countryside together, quickly picking up words from each other. Rufus was proud to show the well-dressed town boy the secrets of the nearby hedgerow. Suddenly he disappeared up into the branches of an old oak tree, needing only three or four nimble leaps before he was high up above the ground. Balbus tried to copy, but could only scramble slowly to a low branch. The view was exciting and Balbus took a careful look around.

They jumped down to the ground and made their way into the cornfield, turned the corner – and met Balbus's tutor face to face. 'Caught you,' cried Septimus, somewhat triumphantly. The tutor did not look pleased. He had awoken early, only to find his young pupil missing from his couch and not to be found in the house. Angry that the boy was not ready for his lessons and guessing that he was exploring outdoors, he had set out to search for him. He too had spotted the smoke over the trees and aimed in that direction, and sure enough found the deserter.

Balbus's face dropped. Before he could introduce his new friend, Septimus pulled Balbus roughly to his side and reached out with his left hand to cuff the other lad. In a flash, Rufus dodged back and was gone without a trace. Septimus pushed Balbus in front of him and marched him back to the Villa, explaining disdainfully that 'no self-respecting person should ever speak to these local people unless to give orders for work. The filth and squalor these Britons live in! They are full of disease and bad habits. Keep away!'

Balbus was disappointed; not only would it be difficult to pursue his new-found friendship, but it hurt him to hear his tutor speak so haughtily. He would have to submit for now, but he promised himself that one day he would return to the camp to see if he could make amends for Septimus's rough manners and patch up the fragile friendship.

Chapter IV

A Great Party

Back at the Villa, Lydia had forgotten her brother. She was far more interested in the preparations going on around her. 'Please can I come to the banquet, Mater? Just for the beginning, pleeease?' she beseeched. Flavia finally agreed, only to be showered with a string of questions about what she was to wear, where she might sit, what food she could have. Flavia was far too busy with her own preparations to worry about Lydia and called a servant woman, 'Please ensure Miss Lydia is attired in her new dress by the dinner hour.' Lydia could scarcely contain her excitement.

By midday the chariots had arrived from Londinium

with Marcus and several of his friends. They were shown to the Baths for a refreshing wash, before dressing for dinner. Later in the afternoon, other chariots arrived with the friends from the neighbouring villa at Farnborough. Lucius and Flavia led their guests into the great Reception Hall. The mosaic floor looked even more splendid in the afternoon sun and, after admiring it, the party gathered around the curved table in the Dining Room. The guests were dressed immaculately. The men wore splendid togas, richly decorated sandals and cloaks of varied colours. The women had their hair drawn back into elegant knots, decorated with small but exquisite items of jewellery. All reclined on couches, watching as the servants carried in trays of exotic foods.

Lydia looked quite lovely, a smaller version of her beautiful mother. Even Balbus looked clean and well groomed, although he was not enjoying the occasion and wished heartily that he was out in the open. He turned his attention to the band of minstrels playing at the end of the room, watching their nimble fingers pluck the strings of their instruments, wondering if he would ever be able to play so well.

Oysters were served, followed by roast pork and trays piled high with fresh fruits. The guests sipped wine, and soon laughter and witty conversation rang up into the roof above. When the guests had eaten their fill, Marcus, looking as if he had left boyhood behind, led the way into the Grand Room where various board games had been laid out for the evening's entertainment. Balbus and Lydia were ushered out of the room and sent to bed.

It was as they turned into the gloomy corridor that Balbus noticed a sandal protruding from behind one of the pillars which decorated the hallway. Lydia was impatient with him, pulling him by the hand, but Balbus turned his head just in time to make out a shadowy figure sliding from behind the pillar. It was Septimus! What was his tutor doing there?

As he lay on his couch that night, the music and peals of mirth resounding through the Villa from the Grand Room, Balbus turned over in his mind the strange sight. Why should Septimus be hiding, spying in their own home? Balbus puzzled out reasons until he could stay awake no longer.

Chapter V
Trouble

Next morning a solemn Lucius and Flavia met the two children at breakfast. Their guests had all departed in the early hours of the morning, and seemed to have taken with them the happiness of the previous evening. Nothing was said until the meal was over, yet both children sensed an air of impending doom.

After what seemed an age, Balbus was called to stand before his father. The strong, well-built man who had often called his servants to order now faced his nine-year-old son. His young boy needed some discipline, but at this moment it seemed as if it had come too late, for the damage had been done. Flavia sat watching, close to tears.

'I understand from Master Septimus that you were out playing with the local boys yesterday?' demanded Lucius.

'Yes sir, well, with one boy,' replied a frightened Balbus, trying hard to put on a brave face.

'Did you have permission from Mater or myself?'

'No, sir.' Balbus hung down his head.

'Since when have children in my family been allowed to do as they please?' This time no answer came. Balbus stared at the floor.

'Did you know that our silver platter has been stolen? It's probably been taken by that boy,' Flavia burst out, unable to contain herself any longer.

So, this explained the strange turn of events. Balbus began to realise the weakness of his position. He knew the enormous value of the silver platter, and it was quite true that he had played with the local boy without consulting any adult. These people were known to steal and loot given the opportunity, yet Balbus felt sure his friend would not take anything from his home – but it was another matter to convince his father of this.

As he wondered what to say, the shadowy figure of his tutor came into his mind, and he wondered if this could explain Septimus's strange behaviour. Pater would never believe that explanation, so Balbus pulled himself up and decided he must face his father's anger.

'Have you nothing to say for yourself?' demanded

Lucius. 'No sir,' came the timid reply. 'Go to your room, and stay there,' growled his father. Lydia turned away, tears springing to her eyes. Why did nice things have to be spoilt? She was so looking forward to their third day in the country, and now everything was turning out to be a disappointment.

Lucius called in some servants. 'Go to the encampment and discreetly search for the platter. It is a large, round, silver dish, decorated with fine patterns and is very valuable.'

Balbus was given little to eat that day. It was clear that he was in great disfavour. The more he suffered, the more determined he became to prove his own innocence and to investigate Septimus's movements of the previous evening.

He was lying on his couch sulking at the injustice of the situation when the door burst open and Lydia arrived, brimming over with the latest news. One of the servants had found Septimus's quarters ransacked, and lying beside his overturned couch lay a hurriedly scribbled note which simply said, 'Help, they're taking me to the woods.'

This was highly dramatic and it made matters look even worse for Balbus. Had his country friend anything to do with this too? He began to wonder himself. For the present he was glad to be in the seclusion of his room. He did not wish to face his parents or the commotion going on in the rest of the house. Once again he turned the whole matter over in his mind.

Later that afternoon, when almost the entire household had been sent to search the woods to the east of the house, Balbus crept silently out of the opposite end of the Villa. Suddenly he winced in pain. A pebble had hit him on the knee. He glanced round. There, hidden in the laurel bush he recognised a familiar pair of eyes. This time Balbus was frightened, but Rufus beckoned him beseechingly. He too had witnessed the strange goings-on, and wanted to find out their cause. 'A silver platter is missing.' Balbus explained as best he could.

Rufus looked thoughtful, turned and ran towards the river flowing close to the Villa, waving to Balbus to follow. As they reached the river's edge, Rufus pointed to something in the mud – a line of footprints made by large sandals and a deep scored line running into the water, the mark of a boat being dragged into the river!

Balbus's imagination began to work overtime. Could Septimus have escaped with the silver platter by boat, leaving the dishevelled room and note as a decoy? He turned to make his way back to the Villa. 'Wait,' cried Rufus. Hidden in a water plant the keen-eyed lad had spotted a small blue bead. Balbus looked at it carefully. 'Septimus!' Only the tutor had beads of that bright shade of blue on his gown. This was the final proof. Balbus squeezed Rufus's hand appreciatively. 'We will meet tomorrow,' he promised and raced home to the Villa.

He went straight to his father and spilled out his story. Lucius rolled the bead around in his hand. 'It is Septimus's bead, but this is little evidence to go on. However, I can see you are in earnest and will send servants out to investigate further.'

Up till now he had blamed the boy for the trouble which had come upon them. Certainly the bead belonged to Septimus, but would the tutor risk his reputation and comfortable job to steal a silver platter? Lucius wondered.

A thorough search of woods, river and the village gave no more trace of either Septimus or the platter. Lucius had to grudgingly admit that the boy from the encampment had been most helpful. It looked horribly as if Septimus, realising the value of the platter, had made a getaway down the little river. Lucius consulted the sundial, confirming the lateness of the day, and sighed, 'He could be on a ship bound for Italy by now.'

The mystery of the stolen silver platter was unfolding. It seemed certain who the thief was. But what mattered more was the platter itself. Where was it? Could the thief be found and the platter recovered? Or was it gone for ever?

Part II
AD 350 – AD 364

Chapter VI

What's Happened to Marcus?

It was an autumn day ten years later. The golden leaves were falling. The last cartfuls of corn lumbered past the Villa accompanied by the grunts of the oxen and shouts from the men. Flavia sat at the window, her face bearing the marks of anxiety and despair. Lucius tried to reassure her, but she had heard nothing of Marcus for more than six months.

In his last letter, Marcus had promised to be home by March, but now the summer was past. She had so looked forward to his return, excitedly anticipating his engagement to Cecilia, a young woman he had met in Londinium. Flavia kept on hoping, but as the servants prepared for their return to Londinium for the winter, she felt she would soon have to face the facts. The weather had been rough – perhaps their vessel had been shipwrecked? If only she could do something to help!

A sudden thought flashed through her mind – what if she had neglected some god and they were angry with her? Normally the family were not religious. There were Roman shrines in town and some of her friends occasionally went to worship the Roman gods and goddesses. Her husband was cynical. 'Religion is a superstitious relic of the past, and now man is well educated and organised, he could well do without such nonsense!'

When Lydia's grandparents had first arrived at Lullingstone, they banished the two marble busts left behind by the Roman general to the Deep Room in the lower regions of the Villa. Occasionally Grandfather had taken food offerings to these venerated ancestors to ensure they remained friendly, but since the young family had moved in, they had received very little attention.

'Perhaps I should take an offering to the gods in the Deep Room,' Flavia suggested to Lucius one afternoon. 'We have neglected them and perhaps they are showing their anger to us.'

Lucius was not impressed with the idea, but said to humour her, 'Well, I suppose it can do no harm,' and sent orders to the servants to open the long-closed doors.

Together they entered the dark and gloomy room. It smelt musty for it was on the same level as the river and in earlier days had been a store for grain. The servant carried a flaming torch which lit up the faces of the two dignified busts of marble, now nearly two hundred years old. One looked severe and annoyed at being disturbed; the other somehow reflected a sympathetic interest in his deep, stone eyes.

Flavia silently pleaded that if he or his departed spirit had any power, he would use it to ensure Marcus's safe return. She placed an ornate vase filled with wine on a ledge and then departed, a tiny ray of hope alight in her heart. 'Clean and redecorate the Deep Room,' she ordered her servants, 'that should placate the gods.'

Balbus returned home, tired after a busy day on the farm. He was almost a man himself and took on a strong, supervisory role. Long past were the days when he played with the local boys. Now they were his servants and he was careful not to let them become too familiar, passing by his former playmates as if they had never met.

Lydia, too, was a fine young woman, an excellent hostess in her own right. Both were concerned for Marcus's well-being, but not quite so anxious as their mother. They had many other activities to fill their minds.

Their lost brother reminded them of the stolen silver

platter and missing tutor of long ago. Neither had ever been traced, though Lucius had sent servants to Rome to make enquiries. He had hoped Marcus might have brought some news of it on his return. The missing platter was a severe loss to the family, especially to Lucius's business. This valuable asset stood as an encouragement to his clients, a token of his ability to guarantee their trade agreements. Since its disappearance, he had been forced to rely much more on the farm for his livelihood.

It was as the family gathered for their evening meal at the Villa that Flavia, as if charged by an electric shock, jumped to her feet and rushed towards the door. In her state of anxiety, she thought she had heard the neigh of a horse in the lane. Could it be Marcus returning?

Lucius took little notice. There were often false alarms. But this time he was wrong. The distant neigh was followed by the clatter of horses' hooves in the lane, and Flavia was there to watch as Marcus rode into the forecourt, alive and well!

The family meal was cold before they returned to the Dining Room. There were so many questions to ask and answer. Marcus explained, between several bursts of interruptions, that his ship had met with a violent storm in the Mediterranean, a wave washing him overboard. 'I was saved by a piece of the smashed mast.' Flavia took in a sharp breath. Marcus smiled at her and patted her hand. 'That kept me afloat, but I drifted for hours, struggling to keep conscious before thankfully some fishermen came to my rescue.'

They took him to their home on the coast of southern Spain, and gave him what food they could spare. He was penniless and alone, with no way home but to walk and beg for food, reaching Britain after all these months. 'Now I have seen all your smiling faces again, especially Mater's, all I wish for is the luxury of a warm bath!' Laughter rang around Lullingstone. The tension was gone. It was good to have Marcus safely home again.

Later that evening, he lay on a couch with his family round a smouldering brazier. The evenings were becoming chilly. Impetuously, Flavia asked if he would like his engagement party to be held at the Villa so that his many friends could use the Great Room. 'We shall have the greatest banquet ever to grace its walls. A celebration of your engagement and safe return home!'

Marcus stiffened. He seemed uneasy as if this suggestion was not welcome. 'Is anything wrong?' pursued Flavia. 'You haven't met a girl you prefer in Rome?'

'No, Mater, it's not that,' replied Marcus. 'I may as well tell you now. You will have to know before long. Whilst I was in Rome, I became a Christian and that will alter a lot of things. It is a long story which I would rather leave until tomorrow but please try to understand.'

'A Christian!' exclaimed Flavia, a new fear gripping her heart. 'I've heard about that new religion. But what difference will being a Christian make?' she demanded. 'Why, I prayed to our Roman ancestors this afternoon, but that won't change my way of life.'

'But Mater, a Christian is someone who has come to know and love the God of the whole universe,' Marcus explained enthusiastically. 'I am indebted to him, for I believe that Jesus of Nazareth was his Son who, though he was God, came into this world to die for sinners like me. I met several people in Rome whose families were descended from those who had seen this Jesus risen from the dead. If God's own Son was willing to do this for me, and I now belong to him, he must become my Lord and Master from now on. Much as I love Cecilia, I cannot marry her until she shares my new-found faith.'

'I have never heard such utter nonsense,' Lucius muttered. 'Your shipwreck has obviously affected your mind. Let's hope you will soon get over it. Young people will believe anything they're told these days. It's a pity I ever let you leave home.'

Balbus and Lydia felt sorry for their brother. He seemed so genuine in what he said. Perhaps he would tell them more when they retired to bed.

Chapter VII

A Big Change

The oil in the lamp burnt low as Marcus told his brother and sister of his new experiences in Rome. He had gone, bored with Londinium, wanting to see the sights of the world's greatest city, and to experience its delights. The first three months of his stay were thrilling, touring the great buildings, watching the Roman army training, experimenting with many pleasures and sports. But after a time, the novelty faded, leaving him feeling empty and lonely.

One evening, a friend invited him to see a chariot race at the Colosseum. The cheering of a thousand spectators filled the arena and his ears. A sudden thought came into Marcus's mind, a comment from an old friend of his father's, Maximus, who had recently turned to the new Christian religion – 'When you go to the arena, remember that the Christians of Nero's time were sent to fight lions in that very same arena. The crowds cheered as wildly then as they do now for chariot races.'

Marcus watched the chariots vying for first place and marvelled at the courage of those Christians persecuted by Nero. How enthusiastic they must have been about their religion to face such a terrible death. The gods in

the shrine at home certainly did not inspire such devotion from him.

Later that evening he was enjoying a long drink in the garden of a Roman villa. It was almost dark but the air was warm. A servant appeared with a message from Maximus. Surprised, Marcus saw that it was an invitation to a Christian church in the city centre. His curiosity having been aroused by his thoughts of the day, he agreed to go.

Next Sunday he went to the hall where the meetings were held, arriving a little late. As he walked into the simple, unadorned building, he heard the voices of several hundred people singing a hymn to their God. He found an inconspicuous corner and watched the proceedings.

The leader read aloud to the gathered people from a letter, written by the apostle Paul (who had twice been a prisoner in Rome): 'Therefore being justified by faith, we have peace with God through our Lord Jesus Christ.'

Marcus glanced around the hall. Amongst the people were some distinguished-looking men and women, but the majority were ordinary citizens and a number were slaves. Everyone seemed deeply concerned. When the preacher prayed, all stood silently and heads were bowed. When he preached, the people listened intently. This was so different from the ritual of the shrines he had visited.

At first, he tried not to listen to the preacher. After all, he had only come to see what these strange people did.

He looked on contemptuously.

But at that moment the preacher seemed to fix his attention on Marcus, and the young man from Britain felt as if he alone was being addressed. The preacher explained that the God who made all things would one day judge all people. They would have to give an account of their lives to their Maker. Marcus began to feel uncomfortable.

'Do I need to explain God's standards and laws?' he was saying. 'Are they not written in the conscience of every human? Who can boast that their life is clean and pure and good?'

Marcus looked down and dared not meet his eyes. But his tone changed and the earnest man explained how God was willing to forgive even the worst offender, the most wretched rebel. Why, he had sent Jesus Christ, his Son into the world only three hundred years ago! He came to make a way for us to be forgiven, living a life of perfect goodness and kindness, healing many diseases with amazing miracles. Yet Pilate, Roman Governor of Judea, had ordered the crucifixion of the Lord Jesus. In the following days, hundreds witnessed his resurrection. They came to a sure knowledge that his death was for them, that he had carried their sins in his body on the cross, and was now in Heaven preparing a place for them.

Marcus looked up again. He was amazed to see the preacher's eyes watering as he explained this with real feeling and concern. But more questions followed.

'Why go on living to enjoy a few short-lived pleasures? Why not turn to the Saviour for forgiveness? Why not trust him and start to live to please him? Yes, perhaps even die for him?'

Marcus ran straight back to his room that night, wanting to forget the whole thing – but he could not. It was as if an invisible person was wrestling with him. He felt so sick when he looked back at his life and saw how little he had achieved. Ashamed at the things which gave him pleasure, he longed to be clean.

'Could the preacher be right?' he thought. 'Was God really willing to receive any sinner who was in earnest?' He tried to fight the feelings, deciding never to go to the church again.

But the following Sunday the urge was irresistible and, much against his will, Marcus found himself once again among the large company gathered. He did not hear much of the address until the preacher came to the words, 'Lord, save me!'

The preacher was describing the frightening experience of the disciple Peter on the lake. Marcus heard only those three words, 'Lord, save me!' He was drawn to them as iron to a magnet. He found himself repeating them, his heart uttering them more earnestly each time – 'Lord, save me!' He began to realise what would happen if God did not answer his prayer. Like Peter, he would be lost.

But God did hear him, and Marcus soon knew God had answered his prayer. He went home, his heart melting with gratitude to the Saviour who had reached out to save him.

The next day he found his way to the church again and told the elder of his strange experience. 'Ah, my friend,' the kindly elder smiled at him. 'This is nothing unusual. It is the work of God. He is calling you; put your trust in him, ask him to forgive you, walk with him day by day, pray to him, and you will know his guiding hand throughout your life.'

Back at Lullingstone the light in the bedroom flickered out. Marcus, exhausted with travelling and emotion, found himself unable to keep his eyes open. Lydia and Balbus now knew his secret. As he fell asleep, Marcus prayed the Lord would save them too.

Chapter VIII
A Sad Day

Crash! Another peal of thunder echoed round the valley only a second after a flash of lightning. For two weeks the rain had been pouring down almost incessantly. There was little to be done on the farm and Lydia and Balbus were weary with waiting indoors. Finally, the rain paused, the sun shone weakly through the clouds, and they went fishing. With the river so swollen, they hoped to get a good catch of trout. Casting their lines and chatting together, they watched their floats from the muddy bank.

There was much to talk about. Marcus had returned to Rome for another brief visit. Word had come that

Septimus, their old tutor, was in the city so Lucius had sent Marcus to investigate, hoping against hope that the silver platter might at last be recovered.

It was now two years since Marcus had returned from his first visit to Rome. Much to his parents' disappointment, he had not given up his Christianity. They were annoyed to watch him gradually giving up his round of social events, though secretly they admitted there were some advantages. Lucius was pleased he worked harder at business. Flavia acknowledged how much kinder and more understanding he had become. But they resented the time he spent with Christian friends in Londinium.

He was also far too friendly with the working men at Lullingstone. It appeared that Christianity was not confined to people of good class. Several of the farm workers, including Balbus's former friend Rufus, met with Marcus and listened as he told them about the life of the Lord Jesus Christ. This deeply disturbed his parents. 'What if Lydia and Balbus get involved too?'

The line jerked and Balbus grabbed for his rod. 'I think I've caught one!' He beamed, reeling in his line. A wet stone moved from under his feet, taking him off balance. Lydia turned to see him fall into the river with a mighty splash.

She laughed, but her laughter soon turned to horror – Balbus was hurt! He lay still in the swiftly flowing river. Jumping down, she tried to tug his heavy body on to the bank. She began to despair of ever lifting the slippery form on to dry land, when a hand reached out and helped her to heave Balbus to safety. Together they lifted him gently out of the water and laid him as comfortably as possible beside the river.

Only then did Lydia notice who had come to her aid. She was alarmed to discover he was a stranger, but looking a second time his face was somehow familiar.

'Stay,' he said. 'I will go for help.' Lydia was anxious, almost tearful, as she looked down at her brother. He lay still and deathly white, all the vibrancy of life gone.

She laid her mantle over him. The rain was again pouring down so heavily that she wondered whether the mantle would protect him for long. She tore her skirt to make bandages. If only she could stop the flow of

blood from his head. With relief, she heard the sound of voices and turned to see two men carrying a make-shift stretcher. One had familiar brown eyes. Now she remembered – Rufus! Balbus's childhood friend. How glad she was he was there to help.

Balbus lay in a semi-conscious state for many days. Flavia and Lucius watched over him. Lydia would scarcely leave his side. But he did not improve. Urgent messages were sent to Rome, and Marcus, travelling day and night, returned to be at Balbus's side at Lulling-stone. His heart ached as he turned into the darkened room and gazed upon the motionless figure. He laid his hand on his brother's shoulder, reciting passages and verses of comfort from the Bible. 'Be strong and of a good courage; be not afraid, neither be thou dismayed: for the Lord thy God is with thee whithersoever thou goest.'

Only weeks before, Balbus had listened with such enthusiasm, his bright eyes radiating interest. Now he was unable to respond, but somehow Marcus knew he heard and understood. Lydia sat in the corner of the room, listening intently, her heart aching. Surely God would not let Balbus die – he was only 21 years old.

A week later the family's spirits rose. Rufus was given permission to visit the sick young man. Balbus's eyes opened, and a sign of recognition passed between them. Gradually he was able to whisper a few words. In his delirium, he had often seen those two brown eyes bending down to lift him to safety, and longed to be able to express his gratitude, to seek forgiveness for his pompous attitude over the past years. No words needed to be uttered, Rufus knew exactly what he was trying to say. He squeezed Balbus's hand, his eyes conveying the message of forgiveness that Balbus sought.

Balbus slipped in and out of consciousness, but he did not look fretful. He knew that just as his friend had forgiven him and come to his rescue, so his Father in Heaven had forgiven his sins and rescued him from hell. Lydia, tending to him faithfully, noticed his calmness and pondered much – had God sent such peace into his heart now he was facing death?

Flavia and Lucius were beside his bed as Balbus slowly passed away. Flavia was distraught, but her youngest son turned to her just before he died and murmured, 'Don't fear Mater. Marcus's Saviour is my Saviour too.' Lydia, with tears silently streaming down her face, prayed that he would be her Saviour also.

Flavia never forgot those words and Lucius was touched by them more than he cared to admit. They both began to realise that Marcus's new religion was something much more than they had imagined. But for people of their importance and position, to become Christians was a very big step. They had seen from their children that it meant a change of heart, affecting every part of life. But they could no longer refuse to believe in the One Almighty God whose handiwork they saw all around them. Secretly they half hoped that he would draw them to himself.

Chapter IX

Mystery Solved

Lydia turned into the country lane. It was spring again and she was off to find Rufus. She always remembered with thankfulness his help on that fateful day the previous autumn, but more recently she had taken an even greater interest in her brother's friend.

With Marcus usually away and busy, Rufus had often taken time to answer her questions about all kinds of things. He seemed to understand how much she missed Balbus. Frequently she found herself the only Christian in the Villa and looked forward to the evenings when she met with Rufus and his friends. Together they prayed to the Lord and read letters from Marcus and other Christians, Lydia reading aloud, Rufus explaining their importance. She admired his enthusiasm as he taught the children from the village to sing the simple hymns he wrote for them.

The sinking sun shed a ray of light on the new green leaves and lit up the bluebell woods which she had so enjoyed on her first day at Lullingstone. Her heart was singing as together they made their way back to Lullingstone. Her happiness knew no bounds when, after tripping over an unseen tree root, Rufus took her hand and kept it gripped in his. She had felt for a while that the Lord wanted her and Rufus to serve him together, but this was the first sign that Rufus was beginning to believe so too.

Lydia was stooping to pick some bluebells when Rufus suddenly beckoned her to lie low. Slinking amongst the trees was a figure she began to recognise. It was Septimus! Grey-haired now but clearly the same man. 'What's *he* doing here?' whispered Rufus. 'Let's follow him.'

Septimus crept through the wood like the fugitive he was, anxious not to be seen, unaware he already had company. Dusk was falling but Rufus's keen brown eyes traced his every movement.

Septimus turned towards the Granary built on stilts, and to their surprise began to crawl beneath it! Lydia's eyes were aching as she searched into the gloom to see what was happening. But Rufus had seen enough. Quickly he ran off in the direction of the Villa. Lydia shrank back into the shadows. She did not want to disturb the man now that she was alone. Oh, when would help arrive?

The Villa doors burst open. Servants with flaming torches rushed across the courtyard in every direction. Septimus was rooted to the spot, immobilised by shock. By the time he recovered, it was too late – he was surrounded. Lucius marched over and ordered the senior servant to take Septimus to his room. He had some important questions to ask.

As they led the tall, stooping figure towards the house, Lydia noticed Rufus was missing. Where was he? All at once, he reappeared – from underneath the Granary clutching a round grubby-looking item. Whatever had he dug up?

Lucius spotted it immediately. 'Aha!' he cried, almost snatching it from Rufus's hands. He hastened towards the light of the Villa, pulling off his cloak as he went and rubbing the mud off the object.

Yes, it was the missing silver platter! 'Look, look,' he cried, and held it up for all to see. He had worried and enquired after it for so many years, and all the time, it had only been a few yards away! Flavia was delighted with Rufus. 'Oh, how can we ever repay you?'

Septimus began to splutter and beg for mercy – 'I have already suffered so much for taking that wretched thing. These past twelve years have been full of anxiety for me!' The Roman to whom he had agreed to sell the silver platter had fumed with anger at his failure to bring it, shipping him off to his estate in Italy to work as a slave. Only a few months ago Septimus had managed to escape, and returned to claim the hidden treasure which by now he felt sure he deserved.

Lucius took little account of Septimus's suffering – 'You have brought all that upon yourself.' He turned to his servants, 'Take him away and lock him up.'

Lydia knew her father would not be lenient with a man who had caused him such loss and trouble over so many years. 'What will happen to Master Septimus now?' she wondered, almost feeling sorry for him.

Lucius was unsure himself. He decided to consult a guest they expected later that week. Marcus had invited

Julius, the Christian elder from the church in Rome, to Lullingstone.

Marcus was keen that his parents should meet Julius, though Lucius had mixed feelings about the visit. He was curious to meet the man who had influenced his son in such a profound way, yet at the same time he was cautious – he did not want to get involved himself! 'If the conversation becomes too religious, I will change the subject to Septimus and the problem of a suitable punishment,' he thought to himself.

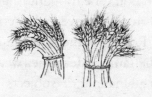

Chapter X

Harvest Time

Flavia and Lucius were surprised as they looked around the Great Room. Gone were the extravagant furnishings of a banquet. Instead, rows of plain wooden benches faced an equally plain table at the front. No sign of lavishly dressed guests – but ordinary men and women from the villages, farm workers, servants from their own household, all led in by Rufus. There were a few from noble families, Flavia noted.

She and Lucius briefly nodded a welcome to their guests. A silence fell upon the gathering as they awaited the arrival of the preacher. Flavia shuddered as she watched her splendid home being quietly surveyed by the entire neighbourhood. The last thing she wanted was their Villa turned into a preaching centre.

She had not fully realised how many people Marcus had reached with his new-found zeal for Christianity. 'If Marcus was a man of business, such success would be worthy of admiration,' she thought to herself.

Flavia unexpectedly enjoyed the company of the preacher from Rome. Somehow Julius had become almost one of the family. Mealtimes were lit up by lively conversation on all manner of subjects – farming, business, fascinating details of life for women in Rome. She knew it would be difficult not to listen as Julius spoke to them about the God he so clearly loved and served.

As the subject turned to Christianity, she glanced at her husband's stern face. They began to regret being persuaded by Marcus and Julius to hold such a ceremony in the Grand Room. Now they had no choice but to sit and listen.

Both Flavia and Lucius tried hard to turn their attention elsewhere as Julius spoke. He read clearly from the Bible and explained its meaning, plainly and simply. And everyone listened! Both rich and poor, educated and uneducated gave their undivided attention to the preacher, following his every word. Before long, they too gave in and listened attentively.

Flavia was not affected until Julius began to explain how God had allowed his only Son to suffer and die on the cross at Calvary in Judea for sinners. Then she was cut to the heart. She thought back to her grief when her own son, Balbus, was so cruelly taken from her by death. She still had an aching heart.

Could it be true that Almighty God had been willing to watch his only dear Son being nailed to a tree by wicked men and then dying in agony – for her sake? It began to dawn on her that dismissing and rejecting such amazing love was a far worse sin than any other she had committed – and that list was great already.

As they retired to bed for the night, she looked shyly at her husband. She did not want to grieve him by becoming a Christian too. He had already 'lost' Marcus, Lydia and Balbus to this 'nonsense', as he called it. She felt it would be too much for him to see her go that way also.

But to her surprise and overwhelming joy, he took her hand and announced, 'I can no longer hold out against the powers of Heaven.' Flavia nodded, unable to speak. 'Would you like me to ask Julius to baptise us as Christians together?' Lucius continued. 'There may be others also who feel so convicted.' Flavia did not ask any questions. Those few words were enough to show Lucius had counted the cost, and was prepared to give up all to follow the Lord.

The angels in Heaven must have rejoiced greatly that night as they looked down on Lullingstone Villa. The harvest was great, not with corn this time, but with sinners who had turned in repentance to the Saviour. Not only was the grand Villa alight with the Gospel, but the surrounding villages of poor Britons also glowed with the warmth of the Saviour's love. Marcus prayed earnestly that this might only be the beginning of the Lord's work in this part of a small island at the edge of the Roman Empire.

Chapter XI

A Grand Plan

Julius checked the final items of his baggage and hoisted them into the chariot, soon to be on its way to the busy harbour of Portus Dubris (Dover). The time had come for him to return to the church at Rome.

Many people, who had eagerly gathered each Sunday to listen to Julius over the past year, now gathered in the courtyard of Lullingstone to bid farewell to the Roman they looked upon as a father. Marcus led in prayer, commending their elder to the Lord, asking for safety in journeyings. But his prayer was not long, for his heart was so moved at this parting that words no longer flowed.

Julius alone presented an air of confidence and joy. He too was sad to leave the little flock of believers at Lullingstone, but confident that the same Lord, who had transformed so many hearts in the months gone past, would continue to bless and lead this new family of his people in the years to come.

As if he read their thoughts and concerns, Marcus addressed the little crowd, 'Before Julius departs, I want to share with you a desire that has been growing within me these past weeks. Now that we are a family of the Lord's people, could we not build a chapel for worship? Could not the Gospel be preached here?'

Lucius added his consent to the plan, 'I feel sure if we work together, we could build a house for the Lord. Perhaps here in the grounds of the Villa, or by extending one of the rooms.'

Lydia clapped her hands for joy. Many people smiled at her enthusiasm, but they too were taken with the idea of their own place of worship.

The buzz of conversation abruptly halted. Septimus walked out of the Villa, bags in hand, and climbed into the chariot alongside Julius. All knew of his crime, and that he had been sentenced to two years' hard labour. Why was he acting as a free man?

Lucius spoke out. 'I am truly indebted to the Lord for graciously saving myself and my family. As a small token of my unworthy love, I am sending Septimus to Rome with Julius.' The thief had shown real signs of sorrow, and was now anxious to be of use. Whilst in

Rome, his task was to negotiate the sale of the silver platter, now restored to its former glory.

'This silver platter has brought so much trouble and sadness, but now the money I receive from its sale will begin the fund for the building of the new chapel.' Even the saddest face lit up as the owner of Lullingstone delivered this piece of good news.

The chariot disappeared along the country lane that morning and the people returned to their work. There remained a certain sorrow, but alongside it feelings of hope and joy emerged. Each started to dream of the chapel that was to be built and the ways in which they could help. Very few had money to offer but they could bring their time, skills and labour. If Julius returned to Lullingstone in years to come, they wanted him to find a house worthy of the Lord.

Chapter XII
Learning to Build

Rufus smiled to himself as he strode along the country lane, humming a hymn of praise. Whoever would have dreamt that Lullingstone Villa would be overrun by local villagers building a Christian Chapel on its roof? Yet this was the project being carried out before his very eyes. He could see Marcus on the roof giving directions to the person manning the pulley that hoisted timber into place. Several men, used to receiving Marcus's instructions on the farm, responded with pleasure as they now worked alongside their master.

In the courtyard below, a dozen carpenters were sawing wood for use in the interior of the Chapel.

Lydia and Flavia were busy organising refreshments for the tireless workers. Lucius looked over plans with an artist who had recently been sent from Rome by Julius. He wanted the church at Lullingstone to be identified as closely as possible with the churches in Rome. The symbol of Christianity, the monogram, Chi-Rho, was to be painted in the Chapel itself and again on the wall of the outer room – the first thing people would see as they reached the top of the small flight of stairs.

The Chi-Rho would link their church to the first Christians in Rome, who met in fear of their lives, worshipping in winding underground tunnels, the Catacombs, engraving their Chi-Rhos in the sandy walls, a testimony of their faith. Many had been martyred for the Saviour.

As the sun shone down on the pleasant countryside around, the believers at Lullingstone did not want to forget those who so suffered that the Gospel might be passed on, proud to take their stand alongside the early believers.

Lucius desired a fresco of the family to be painted on the back wall of the Chapel, asking the artist to portray his family at prayer, with arms upraised. Each member of his family was to be painted between a pattern of pillars.

The youngest member of the family came first, Lydia with her dainty hands. Next Balbus, who could not be forgotten. A curtain drawn behind him indicated that he had passed on to be with the Saviour. Next came

Flavia with Lucius beside her, and Marcus, who now cared for the Lord's flock at Lullingstone, came fifth. Last and most important came the seated figure of the man to whom the whole family owed so much, Julius the elder.

Rufus reached the hive of industry at the Villa, ready to prepare some plaster for the lining of the walls. 'Where's my bag of fine plaster powder?' he exclaimed. It was a costly item – had it been stolen by a local tradesman? Some were bitterly opposed to the building of the Chapel.

A wave of disappointment passed through the workers. They had made real sacrifices to hasten the building along. Some worked late into the evening on the Chapel, even after having risen early to start their farm work. Others made long, exhausting journeys to collect the building materials. No one liked to finish early while Marcus and Rufus worked on, day and night, organising, planning and preparing the rooms which they prayed would be used to bring many lost sheep to the Shepherd.

The missing plaster bag was not the only sign of hatred. Rufus's own family had been deeply divided when he and his friends became Christians. 'You are siding with the rich masters against your own people' was an accusation he often heard. Some of the men in the village refused to work with him, making dark threats.

Nor were the local Christians the only ones to suffer.

Even the Villa family received fewer invitations from their old friends. Lucius was no longer welcomed into the Londinium Forum as he had once been. Many of his associates were puzzled by his new way of life. To them it seemed austere and odd. They wanted to enjoy all the ease and pleasures of Roman life, but not this new religion.

On rare visits to town, Lydia and Marcus looked on with sadness as their friends spent more and more time eating, drinking and squandering their hours. Already, foreign invaders were beginning campaigns to overcome the towns of Britain – would these soon reap victory? Only the Roman soldiers, standing guard around the city walls, gave security. The citizens of Londinium ate and drank on regardless.

But now they were back at their beloved Lullingstone, where all worked with a will, both poor and rich, using their talents to bring into being a building for the Lord of glory. Sometimes there were hindrances along the way.

Another cartload of tiles pulled into the courtyard, the oxen heaving noisily. Marcus, frustrated, tossed one of the tiles back into the cart – 'These are not the right size,' and sent them back to the quarry.

These delays and mistakes made the task seem long and difficult at times, but at the close of the summer the workers began to see their efforts rewarded. The Chapel and its ante-rooms now stood with roof complete, above the Deep Room where the old Roman idols were stored. Marcus remarked to Lucius with satisfaction, 'How good it is to see the Chapel of our Lord above those old Roman gods!' The Lord Jesus had gained supremacy at Lullingstone.

During the cold winter months, work continued inside. Gradually the colourful figures took their places across the walls of the Chapel, and the Christian symbols were painted boldly on the walls. The carpenters and craftsmen prepared the furniture and decorated the Chapel, ready for its opening in the spring.

Flavia, walking arm in arm with Lydia around the rooms, pausing for a moment beneath the painting of Balbus, wondered if the rooms would be ready in time. But all spurred themselves on.

In Londinium, Marcus waited anxiously for the time when he could proclaim the Gospel to a much larger crowd. The little Chapel had many enemies, but he did not mind. As long as the news of its opening was spread far and wide, he felt sure that many would come along. Some would come out of curiosity, even hatred.

'I too went out of curiosity at first,' he remembered, and he prayed many people would return home affected as he had been.

The time seemed to pass slowly, but a new spring arrived eventually, and with it, the Christians at Lullingstone turned their attention from building to visiting, inviting friends and neighbours to their new church. In the market, as well as selling their produce, they spread the news, describing the new building with its staircase and paintings. Soon the entire neighbourhood was buzzing with interest about this new Chapel. Many people had never been up a flight of stairs or even seen a two-storied building. 'What *is* this new teaching? These Christians are so enthusiastic,' they exclaimed.

Finally the great day arrived for the opening of the Chapel. The upper room thronged with people, some coming from afar to see one of the very first Christian Chapels in Britain. The Lord had chosen this busy valley in the countryside of Kent to light a new candlestick in the land.

After a service with hymns of thanksgiving and a time of listening to the preacher explaining a passage of the Bible, Marcus and his fellow-workers praised the Lord for the honour he had bestowed upon them. Their one desire was that the Chapel should be used to bring glory to their Saviour.

The last person to leave the Villa that night was Rufus. His face was now that of a mature man, but his keen, brown eyes still sparkled as his mind turned back to the day when he first hid in the laurel bush and watched the elegant Roman family arrive. 'So much has happened over the years,' he mused.

The family had come into the area and one day might have to leave, but he had been born in the valley and hoped the Lord would allow him to serve him there until his dying day.

He was certain one member of the family would never leave him, for that afternoon Lydia had gladly agreed to

become his wife. The next day he must approach her father to ask for her hand in marriage.

As Rufus neared his home, he confided his sense of nervousness to the Lord who overrules all events. The once proud and haughty owner of Lullingstone Villa had changed in so many ways since he had humbly turned to Christ, but would he agree to his daughter marrying a common workman, whom he had once regarded as uncivilised and uncouth?

Early next morning, Rufus called at the Villa wondering how to begin, but Lucius had already anticipated Rufus's request. 'Welcome, my son, with my hearty blessing for yourself and Lydia,' he said with outstretched arms.

Lucius had come to love Rufus as his own son, finding much in common in their love of the Lord. He was glad to have him as his son-in-law, sure that Rufus and Lydia would be very happy together. Rufus was overjoyed and the wedding was set for the following year.

Chapter XIII

A Wedding

There was not a corner of the Villa that was not in use. Long tables were laid out in the Great Room, and the kitchen was a centre of feverish activity. The courtyard was full of chariots, horses and people.

All in the assembled crowd took a long look at Lydia and Rufus as they emerged from the Chapel. As Christians they had promised to love one another until the day that death parted them. The staircase beneath them was decked with flowers. Soon they were joined by Flavia, Lucius and Marcus on the little balcony. Lydia wore a lovely dress of white linen. Her hair was gathered above her forehead and decorated with pearls.

Rufus stood beside her in a brown robe held by a blue sash. His brown eyes, keen as ever, surveyed the excited crowd in the courtyard, and he squeezed Lydia's hand as he pointed out to her some of their guests.

Amidst a storm of cheers, the bridegroom led his wife down the staircase to the Great Room. Even this vast room seemed to shrink in size as visitor upon visitor poured in to enjoy the wedding feast.

A ripple of surprise began to pass around the guests. Entering the room and being welcomed to a seat of honour close to the bride, was the elder, Julius! Lydia

sprang to her feet to embrace him. His presence put the finishing touch to the joyfulness of the day. Before the feast began, he rose to give thanks to the Lord for his wonderful ways.

Later in the afternoon, Lydia and Rufus asked him to address the party. Even the members of the family who were against Christianity listened as Julius spoke to the couple and told them how much it meant to him to be present on this joyous day. Many of the guests were curious to know what lay in the parcel which sat at his fingertips.

With a twinkle in his eye, he tantalised Rufus and Lydia, saying, 'This marriage gift is not for you alone, but for you to share with all the believers here at Lullingstone – and in all Britain!'

He continued, adding to the riddle, 'I am only a poor pastor, yet I have brought you the most precious gift in the world!' promising if they treasured and obeyed it, their marriage would grow and deepen and be used by the God of Heaven and earth for his glory.

Silence fell over the entire company as Rufus and Lydia stood to receive their mysterious gift from Julius. With great care, Lydia removed the wrapping and before her lay books with newly inscribed Latin words. Rufus was first to realise what the manuscripts contained. He looked carefully through the pages and raised a querying look to Julius. Julius nodded.

Rufus was a robust young man not normally given to emotion, but as he stood to explain to his guests the meaning of Julius's riddle, his eyes looked distinctly moist.

'In this hand I hold a copy of the Gospel of John, containing the very words of our Lord Jesus Christ,' he told the people, raising up the book. 'And in this hand, I hold Paul's epistle to the church at Rome, full of much teaching for us.'

These books had been sent to the Christians in Britain from the church in Rome. Rufus was overwhelmed with gratitude. 'Please read the Holy Scriptures to us, Master Julius.'

Every ear listened attentively as Julius read of when the Lord Jesus attended a wedding at Cana of Galilee. Next, he turned to a passage towards the end of Paul's epistle beseeching the people of God to present their lives as a 'living sacrifice' to the Lord their God.

As Julius laid down the precious pages, the new couple, together with all their Christian guests, promised the Lord to do just that. Then, as if to seal their vow, Rufus drew his bride towards him and kissed her.

PART III
AD 372 – AD 410

Chapter XIV

A Strange Caller

Many years had rushed by and with the passing time changes had come to the Villa. New family members had come and others departed. Lydia's twin sons, Paul and James, were now ten years old and filled the Villa with their cheerful voices, but Lydia's mother had died quite suddenly one autumn morning the previous year. The funeral had been a happy one, for Flavia dearly loved the Lord. People from all around the valley had come, some curious to see how Christians faced death, others wanting to pay their respects to this much loved lady of the valley. Older friends could not but compare this quietly joyous event with the time, many years before, when Flavia had buried her younger son, Balbus, only in his twenties.

That funeral had been a scene of grief and despair, surrounded by elaborate ritual, kept alive by visits to the Temple-Mausoleum which stood so close to the Villa, where dark incantations were frequently repeated. These visits had ceased when Flavia became a Christian, and by contrast her funeral was simple and comforting. Even the boys listened attentively as Uncle Marcus described Heaven, picturing their grandmother standing before her Saviour, dressed in the white robes he had purchased for her on Calvary's cross. They gazed at Balbus's portrait on the Chapel wall. Now, Marcus reminded the congregation, his mother was with Balbus, able to tell him how his dying sentence had been used by the Lord to convert her.

Rufus often told his sons, 'Be good to your Mater, boys. She is missing her own Mater, more so now that your great-aunt has come.' The two boys understood perfectly. They too compared their sweet, unselfish grandmother, whose delight had been to serve the Lord, with her younger sister, Aunt Augusta, now living with them, who haughtily insisted on her own comforts and refused to attend Chapel.

Though Lydia had not complained, the children had noticed she held back her tears as Aunt Augusta insisted on opening the Deep Room beneath the Chapel. 'My priest will call from time to time to make offerings to the spirits of the household, so shamefully neglected here,' she announced.

Paul was outspoken on several occasions, urging his parents to 'Send her back to Londinium!' Lydia, with wisdom, urged him to be more understanding. 'Aunt Augusta is an old, lonely lady. She has lost her husband and home to the raiders in Londinium. In time, she too might seek and find the Lord.'

It was towards the start of spring when a loud knock came at the door of the Villa. The boys were inside, busy with their Latin grammar, longing to finish and escape to join their father on the farm. Lydia sat with them, mending clothes. She set her sewing aside and went to see who had called. The boys were curious. Who could it be? They tiptoed quietly to the curtain and listened carefully. It was a stranger's voice. However hard they tried, they could not hear what was being said. Soon they heard their mother bidding her caller farewell and scampered back to the table, their faces a picture of innocence.

Lydia returned to the room with an anxious look on her face. 'Go quickly and fetch your father.' Paul and James, pleased to finish their Latin early, rushed outside. They discovered their father behind the Granary, repairing a large beam of wood in danger of collapsing. Without stopping either to look at the farm carts or to search for eggs amongst the hay, they ran straight to him, their task too important to delay.

Rufus put down his tools and returned to the Villa. Who was the stranger? What was the news he brought that troubled Lydia so?

78

Chapter XV

Bad News

Much as Paul and James wanted to discover the news the stranger brought, they agreed to disappear whilst Lydia shared her concerns with Rufus. Quickly they bounded away and were soon chasing one another up the steps leading to the Chapel. Each knew what the other had in mind – to tidy the room and lay out the stools ready for the worship services on Sunday.

New people had begun coming since Flavia's funeral. The words of the hymns and the atmosphere of Christian joy mingled with natural sadness had moved them, setting them thinking. When Marcus invited them to come to a Sunday service, they accepted. Any feelings of shyness soon melted away, and Sundays became the bright day of their week, for them and for their children.

Paul and James were happy to have new young friends to share in the lessons that Lydia taught.

Rufus appeared at the entrance porch, his face somewhat tense. He beckoned to them and before long they joined their mother in the kitchen, where she and a servant were preparing a meal. James noticed that Lydia's eyes looked a little red but her calm bearing comforted him. 'Well Mater, what *is* the matter? Why did that stranger call? Was he a messenger from town?' they demanded.

They sat around the large cooking grate and Rufus, smiling to reassure his sons, began to answer their queries. Yes, the messenger had come from Londinium and yes, the news was not good. Lucius's best customer in Italy had gone out of business leaving a large debt unpaid. 'Business has been dwindling for several years. Rome is no longer powerful,' explained Rufus. 'And this is a major blow, coming so quickly after the cancellation of our grain orders to France.'

'Will Grandfather be bankrupt?' Paul enquired anxiously.

'No,' replied Rufus, 'he has enough to pay his immediate bills, but it will make a difference here at the farm. We will have to cancel the rebuilding of the Granary. Mater is worried there will not be enough money to pay all the farm workers. Perhaps some of the land will have to be sold or left uncultivated.'

The boys frowned, old enough to see the difficulties that lay ahead. Playing amongst the children of the valley, they would be the first to notice any tension and discord. Many of Rufus's relatives had been touched and moved by the change in the family at the Villa. Gone were the days of unashamed luxury and lavish parties. Any slaves had been given their freedom, and the ladies of the Villa took care of people who were sick. But Paul and James knew from the unguarded conversations of their young cousins, that some of Rufus's family still hated him for becoming a Christian and marrying the daughter of the Villa. If their security were threatened, this hostility could so easily be fanned into action against the Villa.

'Will I have to give up my new mini-chariot?' young James enquired, wondering how this might affect him.

'We shall see,' said Rufus, 'but don't lose heart. Grandfather and Uncle Marcus will be arriving here tonight and, more importantly, we know that the Lord is our protector.' Lydia smiled and nodded.

Chapter XVI

Working for Good

Early next morning the whole family gathered in the Reception Room. Lydia handed her precious wedding gift, the Book of Romans, to Marcus who turned to the eighth chapter and read the closing verses:

'In all these things we are more than conquerors through him that loved us. For I am persuaded, that neither death, nor life, nor angels, nor principalities, nor powers, nor things present, nor things to come, nor height, nor depth, nor any other creature, shall be able to separate us from the love of God, which is in Christ Jesus our Lord.'

Everyone was listening intently. How familiar these words were, but somehow they took on a new meaning that day. Lydia felt ashamed of her tears. Rufus wondered if he had explained the news properly to the boys.

Marcus led the family in prayer. Soon all worries were forgotten as Marcus praised the Lord for his goodness to them down the years, and his wonderful grace in showing mercy to this family when so many lived in fear and despondency.

'We would humbly ask,' he prayed, 'these events would work in such a way to increase our trust in thee, and to lead others to find our dear Saviour for themselves.'

After a few moments of subdued silence, Paul's clear voice rang out. 'Please Grandfather, may I suggest something?'

'Well, yes,' replied the surprised old gentleman.

'Why don't we pull down the Baths, fill them in with soil and let Mater plant a vegetable garden there?' Everyone looked startled, but Paul continued quickly, before anyone could interrupt.

'I know the Baths cost a lot to run as I have to stoke them up with wood. We would save on our fuel bill. They need repairing, more cost. Better to spend the money on the farm equipment which we need.'

He came to a halt, slightly out of breath.

Grandfather nodded, pleased with the boy's clear reasoning and unselfish attitude. A year before, Paul had confided that he had put his trust in the Lord. His reaction to the crisis showed to all that, despite his youth, a very real change had taken place in his life.

'That's a very wise suggestion,' came the appreciative

answer, 'and I know how you boys enjoy your fun in the Baths – especially when you have friends here. If we do go ahead with this plan, you'll have to come and visit me in Londinium more often and I'll take you to the Baths there.'

Next it was Rufus's turn. His brown eyes, which still twinkled, reflected much earnestness. He too had been pondering the situation at Lullingstone and, although he still felt an unworthy member of the family, he wanted to make a proposal that had lain long on his heart, shared only with the Lord.

'We all know,' he started shyly, 'that the Christians in Londinium and Dorset need Marcus. Yet it is becoming impossible for him to manage the farm and do the Lord's work too. The other elders of the church here are anxious to bear their responsibilities and would be glad to send Marcus out for missionary work in the towns and villages of England.'

All eyes turned on Marcus. Everyone knew that his heart was in the Lord's work, yet his duties at Lullingstone held him back. A smile of delight could clearly be seen crossing his face, but then he looked serious and puzzled, 'I don't really understand how this would be possible,' he finally replied.

Rufus's shyness had vanished and he began to explain his plan to a captivated audience. 'Don't you see that this financial catastrophe could be the answer to our prayers? It means we can scale down the farm work. It means that we need not keep the Villa in its present grand style. Grandfather finds it difficult to travel here and soon Paul and James must leave for school in Londinium.'

The twins did not know whether to look sad or glad at this news. They loved the Villa and their work on the farm, yet Londinium offered a great challenge, and being young boys they were fascinated by the great city. But their father continued, 'If the Baths were closed, as Paul suggested, along with some of the larger rooms, and the farm work reduced, then Marcus would be free to travel wherever he is needed.'

'Then what about the Chapel?' Marcus enquired. After years of painstaking labour, he did not want to abandon the work dearest to his heart.

But Rufus had this topmost in his plan. 'Lydia and I would be glad to live here in the smaller rooms at the side of the Villa, so that the Chapel will be constantly watched and cared for. The time I shall spend on the farm will enable me to keep up my ties with everyone living in the valley, and I will still have time to study and teach the Word.'

'Could we come here and help during our school holidays?' Paul and James interrupted.

'Of course,' replied Lydia. 'It would be just like the days when I was a child and came for holidays at the Villa.'

The boys smiled. All kinds of ideas were flooding into their minds and they asked to leave the room so that they could talk these over. Rufus and Marcus followed the twins out of the Villa. They strolled down to the river's edge. They, too, had a lot to discuss. Marcus had always liked his brother-in-law, his appreciation for him growing over the years. He felt certain he could leave the people of Lullingstone safely in Rufus's care.

Lydia made her father comfortable before she went to prepare the family meal. He was an old man now and needed his rest. As he fell asleep a peaceful smile replaced the strained expression of the previous evening. He did not want to disappoint his family or put their happiness at risk. But instead of reacting with dismay to his financial crisis, they had welcomed it. He was so glad that the Lord's work meant more to them than anything else.

Only Great-Aunt Augusta looked sulky and depressed at supper that night. 'How can anyone be excited at the loss of money?' she muttered within herself. 'Humph, it's that Chapel, waste of time!' And as she had no part in the excitement, she retired to her own room, away from all the noise and bustle.

As the sun sank behind the hills that evening, Lydia and Rufus slipped out of the Villa. Rufus turned away to the barn to prepare the cart for the morning when he would collect the children and adults for the morning service.

In the twilight Lydia could just see well enough to pick a bunch of bright yellow daffodils. They would look beautiful inside the Chapel. She was weary at the end of a busy and taxing day, but still the task of preparing the Chapel had to be done. But where was the broom? Oh, there it was, in the far corner. Someone had swept the room already. Her heart warmed as she realised Paul and James had done the work for her.

Cheerfully she placed the Scriptures on the reading desk, handling them carefully. Copies had been made, shared with other churches, but this one was very precious to her. In the half-light she read the words which meant so much, especially at the close of this particular day, 'And we know that all things work together for good to them that love God, to them who are the called according to his purpose.'

Lydia knew the future would not be easy. Many changes would soon be taking place around her, but she thanked the Lord for all that had occurred that day and read the verse again slowly. She closed the book in readiness for the morning and as she descended the Chapel steps she repeated the verse, again and again.

PART IV
AD 410

Chapter XVII

Fire!

And so the years passed by. Lydia and Rufus spent many happy years in the Villa, watching their sons grow and marry, and then in turn a new generation of children. The Baths were filled in, the Granary blew over after one fierce autumn storm, and the farm work declined as Lydia and Rufus grew older. But the Chapel work continued and prospered, filled with people young and old who turned to the Saviour.

But elsewhere in Britain, peace was crumbling into fear and anxiety. That very year, AD 410, Emperor Honorius had withdrawn the Roman army from Britain – they would now have to defend themselves. To Lydia, this was no surprise. She had watched the wealth and orderliness of the Romans slowly disintegrating. The merchants in Londinium turned to a life of leisure, but now were heavily taxed and there was little money to spare.

Already the Saxons were raiding the south coast. The road leading back to Londinium was in a state of disrepair. People, afraid, moved further west. Lydia was thankful that Paul and James had taken their wives and little ones to the relative safety of Wales. One thing more gave Lydia comfort – the Gospel which the Lord had graciously brought to Britain would be guarded and

spread by the Celtic people wherever they travelled.

Then one spring, Rufus died, catching a fever after being caught in a rainstorm. Lydia often sat by his grave on the hillside above Lullingstone Villa, reflecting on God's goodness to them through their life together. She was now 77 years old, content to wait until she too would join him in Heaven. The bluebells had been especially fine that year. Yet it was to be the last time Lydia would see them at Lullingstone.

'Mistress, mistress, wake up quickly.' Moriah the servant shook her awake. 'The Saxon raiders are coming, we must flee!' In the dim light of the dawn, with fear and trembling fingers, Lydia clumsily put on her clothes and shoes. As she rushed to the door, she paused and turned back towards the Chapel – 'The manuscripts,' she cried, hurrying up the Chapel stairs to get her precious wedding present – the Word of God. The pages were crinkled around the edges, the parchment yellowed with age but the words stood out strong and bold. The Saxon raiders would not destroy this!

Sounds of galloping horses and shouts of angry men reminded Lydia of her danger, and she ran for hiding to the woods above the Villa.

Soon Lullingstone Villa was ablaze. Lydia took one last sorrowful look at her home of many years. 'The Lord, who I love, who is so faithful, still reigns over all the nations. The glory of the Romans may pass, but my Lord's words will keep his people and bring them to eternal glory.'

Fellow Christians came with horses and offers of help for their elderly friend. She began her long journey to join her sons in Wales, lifting up her heart to her Lord and praying, 'Revive thy work in this land again. Bring the light of the Gospel once more to this very valley.'

Reconstruction in the British Museum of the wall painting from the Chapel at Lullingstone Villa, showing the figures painted on the Chapel wall. They are each shown in the attitude of an early Christian at prayer. One (Balbus in our story) has a curtain painted behind him indicating that he had died. (Photos: Chris Laws)

POSTSCRIPT

AD 410 to now

Uncovering the Secrets of Lullingstone Villa

Our story is now at an end. Soon the charred remains of the Villa and its Chapel were covered with soil washed down from the surrounding hills. Over the years, grass began to grow among the ruins and in time the house became a mere bump on the landscape. Trees grew up and hid any remaining signs of the life which had once revolved around this spot of land.

It was not until over 1,300 years had passed, in the year 1750, that a group of workmen who were erecting a fence at Lullingstone Park uncovered part of the beautiful mosaic floors. However, it was nearly another 200 years later, in 1939, when a tree was blown down by fierce winds, that archaeologists began to take an interest, curious to discover what secrets of the past were buried beneath the ground.

In 1949 Lt. Col. Meates and his team began to dig and explore. With the utmost care they unearthed the Roman Villa and started to piece together the tiny fragments which had lain still since the day of the fire.

The great catastrophe, which was so terrible for the people of Lullingstone hundreds of years ago, brought an unexpected blessing. The burning flames caused the house to collapse suddenly and remain smashed but preserved underground, until the twentieth century. Had the house decayed slowly there would have been little left for future generations to discover. Instead the team of historians were able to bring to light not only the splendid mosaic floors, but also the pictures and symbols which once decorated the Chapel.

By paying the greatest care to every detail as it was discovered, the history of the Villa was traced from its simple start in AD 80-90 to its sudden end in the fire of AD 410. After years of sifting minute pieces of stone and charred remains this grand jigsaw of history was pieced together.

The most remarkable fact which emerged was the existence of the Chapel. Because it was built above the Deep Room which simply housed the ancestral busts of its former Roman owner, the Chapel had collapsed into the space waiting beneath it, and could be painstakingly put together. It was a great surprise to the experts to realise that a Christian Chapel existed so many years ago in Britain. The spread of Christianity was thought to be very small in our land and many of us learned at school that it was not until AD 597, when Augustine arrived on our shores with his Roman Catholic beliefs, that Christianity came to Britain. Lullingstone is a monument to the fact that not only were there Christians in Britain in Roman times, but that even in the countryside a Chapel had been built where ordinary folk could worship. Despite the terrible persecution of Christians in Rome, the Gospel had spread to this westerly corner of the Roman empire.

Since the discovery of the Lullingstone Chapel more recent archaeological finds have shown that there were Christian communities elsewhere in the British countryside. At Hinton St. Mary in Dorset a large mosaic pavement bears the same Chi-Rho symbol as found at Lullingstone. At Water Newton in Cambridgeshire, a Roman town, a hoard of silver vessels and plaques also bore the Chi-Rho symbol and longer inscriptions. Other discoveries also have shown that Christianity spread in Britain far more widely than historians previously thought. (Literary evidence shows that Christian leaders from Britain attended a Church Council in southern France as early as AD 314.)

Broadbent in *The Pilgrim Church* traces the spread of the original early Celtic British Christianity to Wales, Ireland and Scotland. When Augustine arrived in England there was disagreement between his followers and the early Christians who remained closer to the

95

Scriptures. 'The British order continued its resistance, until in the 13th century its remaining elements were absorbed into the Lollard movement.'

This early Gospel flame was not extinguished. When John Wycliffe, the 'morning star' of the Reformation, began his work in the 1300s, he found most support and interest amongst those who could trace their spiritual ancestry back to this early Celtic British Christianity that began in places like Lullingstone.

In our story we have clothed the ruins and remains with imaginary life and people, our only clue to their identity being the six figures painted on the Chapel wall. We could suppose that these were the inhabitants of the Villa at the time, with the exception of the seated figure whom we have assumed to be the elder of the church at Rome. One day in Heaven we shall have opened to us the real story of Lullingstone and its people, when we 'know all things'. 'Now I know in part; but then shall I know, even as I am known' (1 Corinthians 13.12).

In the meantime we remind ourselves that we are surrounded by a 'great cloud of witnesses', though unseen by us. Those who laboured in centuries long past are an inspiration to us to labour and serve the same Gospel which first found its way to our island so long ago.

This story is based on the historical facts derived from the archaeological discovery of the Lullingstone site. The wall pictures from the Chapel and the Roman busts can be seen in the Roman Room of the British Museum in London.

The full account of the archaeological exploration of this site is described with vigour and interest by Lt. Col. Meates in his book *Lullingstone Roman Villa*, published by Heinemann Ltd (though now out of print).

Lullingstone Villa is open to the public. It is situated near Eynsford village close to the A224 on Lullingstone Lane, DA4 0JA.

www.english-heritage.org.uk/visit/places/
lullingstone-roman-villa/

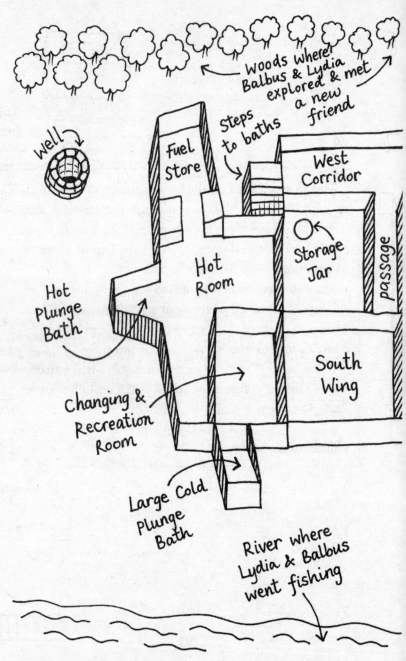

Well

Woods where Balbus & Lydia explored & met a new friend

Fuel Store

Steps to baths

West Corridor

Storage Jar

passage

Hot Room

Hot Plunge Bath

South Wing

Changing & Recreation Room

Large Cold Plunge Bath

River where Lydia & Balbus went fishing

Lullingstone Map by Naomi Berry

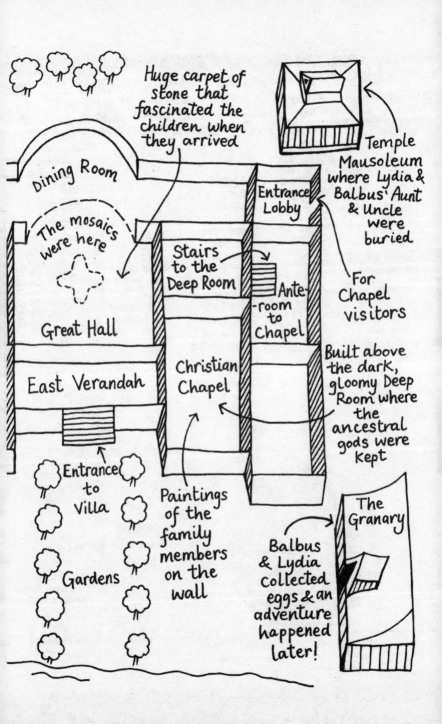

Approximate Dates	AD 80 to 90	AD 180	AD 200 to 280	AD 280

Historic Table of Events

From: 'Lullingstone Roman Villa' by Lt. Col. G. W. Meates

Roman rule began in Britain AD 43

Building of a flint and mortar house. The Deep Room constructed for use as a grain store by native farmer becoming romanized.

A wealthy Roman of Mediterranean origin expanded the house, adding Baths, Kitchens and the north cult rooms. The Deep Room became a place of worship – the marble portraits were probably brought in.

The house thought to be left derelict except for establishment of a Tannery.

Reoccupation by a Romano-British family who practised farming on a large scale – whose descendants continued to own the villa until the 4th century. At this time the Baths were rebuilt and the marble portraits deposited in the Deep Room. The Granary was built.

Lullingstone Villa Timeline

Events from our Story

The Villa was acquired by our family's grandparents, who restored the Villa, rebuilding the Baths. The farming was so successful that they were able to send their son to Londinium for his education.

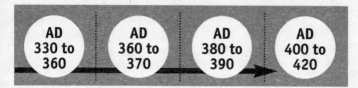

| AD 330 to 360 | AD 360 to 370 | AD 380 to 390 | AD 400 to 420 |

Roman rule ended in Britain AD 410

The owner used the house as an intermittent residence, farming continuing. The apsidal Dining Room and the Reception Room with mosaic floors were constructed.

Foundation of the Christian Chapel and its associated rooms. Pagan rites continue in the Deep Room.

The Baths pulled down and filled in. The Granary gradually pulled down. The Christian rooms still in use.

The final fire.

Gradually the hillside covered the Villa and hid the house and Chapel until its discovery hundreds of years later in AD 1750 and 1949. It was a surprise to all that Christianity had been in Britain at such an early date.

The Villa was inherited by Lucius – mosaic floors laid, other building work completed. First visit of the family to the house (AD 340, Lydia aged 7). Marcus returns to tell of his conversion to Christianity (AD 350).

Chapel building completed. Wedding of Lydia and Rufus.

News comes of Grandfather's financial crisis. Marcus leaves farmwork at Lullingstone. Rufus and Lydia use only small area of house. Work on the farm diminishes but Chapel work goes on.

Rufus dies (AD 406). Lydia watches the house burn (AD 410, Lydia aged 77).

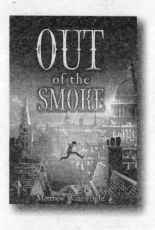

Out of the Smoke
Matthew Wainwright

336 pages, paperback, Wakeman, ISBN 978 1 913133 10 8

'Billy stood on the ridge and looked north, to where the dome of St. Paul's rose over the city, surrounded by a forest of chimneys disgorging a steady stream of pale smoke into the darkening sky.

'The chimneys were calling to him. It was time to go back.'

Plunged into the criminal underworld of Victorian London, with notorious gang leader Archie Miller closing in on him, every turn Billy the chimney sweep takes only leads to more trouble. When the 'Poor Man's Earl' offers him a chance to exchange his gangland life for an education, Billy must decide if his pride is too high a price to pay, and whether turning on Archie will mean freedom or death.

This fictional story of faith and survival is based on the work of the Seventh Earl of Shaftesbury. For children aged 12+, but adults will appreciate and enjoy this too.

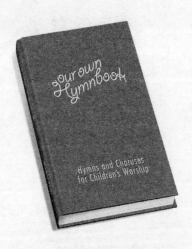

Our Own Hymnbook
Hymns and Choruses for Children's Worship
Words-only Edition
Compiled by Jill Masters

127 pages, 'leatherette' cover, sewn binding, full colour, Wakeman,
ISBN 978 1 870855 69 3

- ℘ 'In this book we have chosen some of the very best hymns and choruses for you, written by men and women who greatly loved the Saviour' (from Introduction).

- ℘ Attractively laid out with full colour.

- ℘ Arranged in subject order, beginning with hymns for the youngest children.

- ℘ Suitable for use in Sunday School and for personal devotional reading.

- ℘ With passages from God's Word added.

Our Own Hymnbook
Hymns and Choruses for Children's Worship
Music and Words Edition

233 pages, spiral bound paperback, Wakeman,
ISBN 978 1 870855 68 6

Our Own Hymnbook contains both old and new items, chiefly well-known and memorable compositions loved over decades. It incorporates many of the famous choruses produced by the CSSM from the 1930s, excellent examples of how Gospel precision and commitment of heart may be united in verse.

Nothing matches the traditional genre of hymn and chorus writing for spiritual accuracy, clarity, reverence and quality. Many of these songs of worship have lived on in the memories of children even to old age, serving as beacon lights of saving truth. This compilation contains 97 hymns and 99 choruses, placed in spiritual categories.

Lessons for Life
Sunday School Lesson Notes
by Jill Masters

Paperback, sewn binding, Wakeman

Book 1 207 pages, ISBN 978 1 870855 07 5

Book 2 222 pages, ISBN 978 1 870855 11 2

Book 3 252 pages, ISBN 978 1 870855 15 0

Book 4 252 pages, ISBN 978 1 870855 20 4

Four-year lesson notes and visual aids for evangelistic Sunday School classes (aged 4 to 16). Acclaimed as 'the best' by numerous conservative and reformed pastors.

Honed over 30 years in Britain's largest children's Sunday School and teenage Bible Classes at the Metropolitan Tabernacle, London, these have reached youngsters from rich and poor homes alike, including thousands of unchurched. All lessons are primarily evangelistic, consistent with the doctrines of grace, and teach the great doctrines and events of the Bible in a memorable way.

Four volumes give four years of notes, and include

illustrations and instructions for visual aids. These notes are used throughout the UK (and in many other countries), standing almost alone in providing powerful evangelistic applications and arguments which children and young people can really respect.

High quality, colour visual aids and Bible Learning Course sheets accompany the lessons (visual aid above is for the lesson on Jacob's Ladder from Genesis 28).

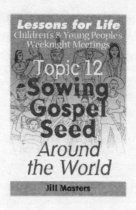

Lessons for Life
Weeknight Meeting Topics Teachers' Notes

by Jill Masters

A4 folders

These topics have been developed for weeknight meetings (teenagers and younger children). These have proved highly popular and effective (with speakers and hearers alike) over many years in London's largest Sunday School and many others also. They never fail to engage the minds of the young. Mrs Jill Masters has done the homework for speakers, providing them with fascinating ideas which will captivate children.

Twelve topics available. See Sunday School page of the Metropolitan Tabernacle website for further details.

Lessons for Life
Junior Church

by Jill Masters

A4 packs, local photocopying allowed

This unique eight-year plan of lessons, based on the great doctrines of the faith, has proved popular with the Tabernacle's morning Sunday School for children of service attenders, giving them a sound foundation for life, and respect and love for the Lord and his Word. Here are the main features:–

ℬ   A syllabus of topics divided into four age groups, designed for 3 to 12 year olds. These could also be used in holiday Bible clubs and home schooling.

ℬ   An outline lesson together with attractive and varied weekly worksheets for the children.

The full range of Sunday School materials, as well as free lesson videos for children and teenagers can be found at MetropolitanTabernacle.org/Sunday-School